for James Lyke and Don Heitler

ARRIVAL OF THE QUEEN OF SHEBA

G.F. HANDEL
Arranged for Two Pianos/Four Hands
by RICHARD SIMM

for James Lyke and Don Heitler

ARRIVAL OF THE QUEEN OF SHEBA

G.F. HANDEL
Arranged for Two Pianos/Four Hands
by RICHARD SIMM